GREAT CENTRAL RAILWAY

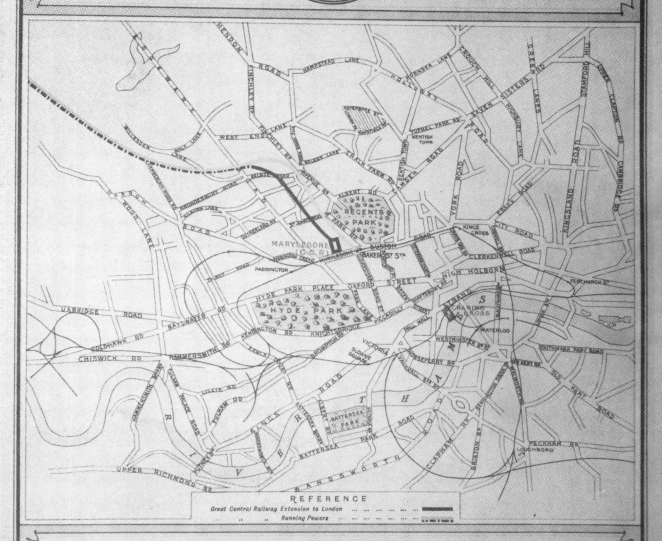

REFERENCE

Great Central Railway Extension to London ... ...
" " Running Powers ... ...

MAP OF LONDON & DISTRICT

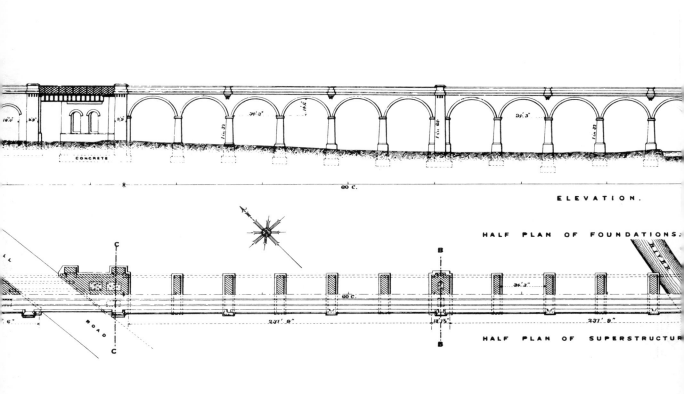

ELEVATION.

HALF PLAN OF FOUNDATIONS.

HALF PLAN OF SUPERSTRUCTURE.

CONCRETE

THE MAKING OF
A RAILWAY

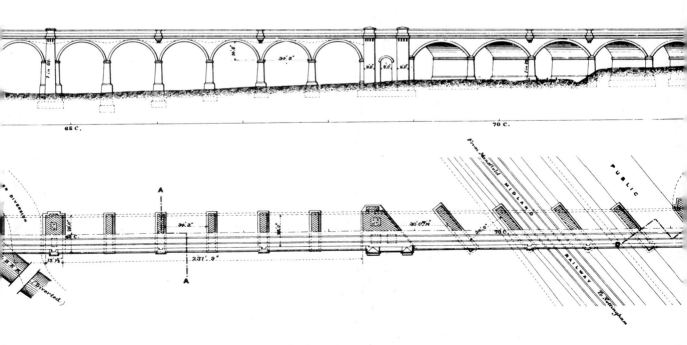

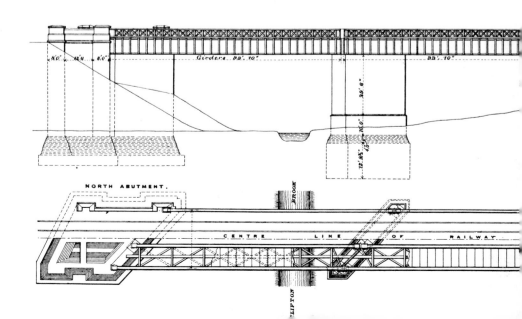

NORTH ABUTMENT.

CENTRE   LINE   OF   RAILWAY

THE MAKING OF
A RAILWAY

L.T.C. Rolt

PHOTOGRAPHED BY S.W.A. NEWTON

ALAN SUTTON

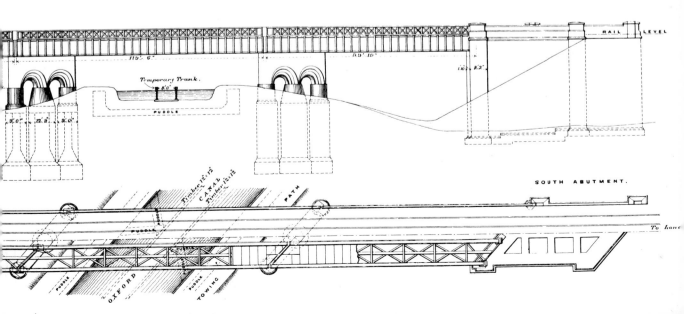

This edition first published in the United Kingdom in 1990
Alan Sutton Publishing Limited · Brunswick Road · Gloucester

This edition first published in the United States of America in 1990
Alan Sutton Publishing Inc. · Wolfeboro Falls · NH 03896–0848

First published in 1971 by Hugh Evelyn Limited
Published in this edition by Alan Sutton Publishing 1990

British Library Cataloguing in Publication Data

Rolt, L. T. C. (Lionel Thomas Caswell, *1910–1974*)
  The making of a railway
  1. England. Railway services: Great Central Railway
  London extension. Construction, History.
  I. Title
  625.1'00942

ISBN 0-86299-582-5

Library of Congress Cataloging in Publication Data applied for

Original Design by E.W. Fenton
Design – this edition by Martin Latham

PUBLISHER'S NOTE

The photographs in the book form part of a collection presented by the photographer himself,
before he died in 1960, to the Leicester City Museum. Some of these photographs have been
published previously, notably in the Museum's own booklet, *The Last Main Line*. The
publishers wish to thank the Museum for making the whole collection available and for
allowing the reproduction of those which have been selected for this book. The engravings of
plans, elevations and other structural elements are reproduced, by kind permission of the
Institute of Civil Engineers, from the Institute's *Minutes of Proceedings*, Volumes CXII and
CXLIII, 1899–1901. The map of the line and other endpapers have been kindly supplied by
Mr E.W. Fenton from the original invitation to the opening of the line.

Typesetting and origination by
Alan Sutton Publishing Limited
Printed in Great Britain

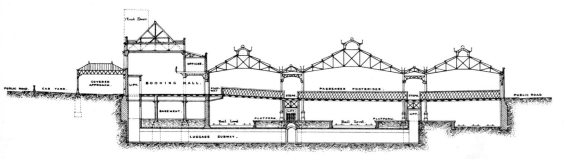

Contents

Drawings and diagrams: The Bulwell Viaduct *pages 2 & 3*; Oxford Canal Viaduct *title page*; Nottingham Victoria Station *opposite*; Marylebone Station *this page*; Embankment and Cutting details *page 88* Rail Sections *page 134*; Endpapers, *front* Map of the completed line and detail of the Marylebone area, *back* Invitation to the opening of the line.

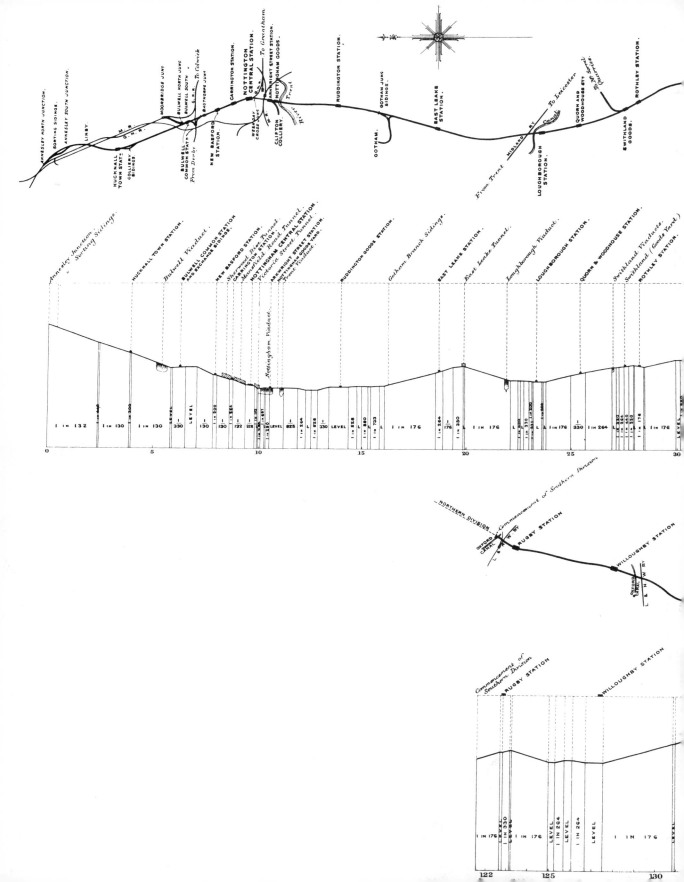

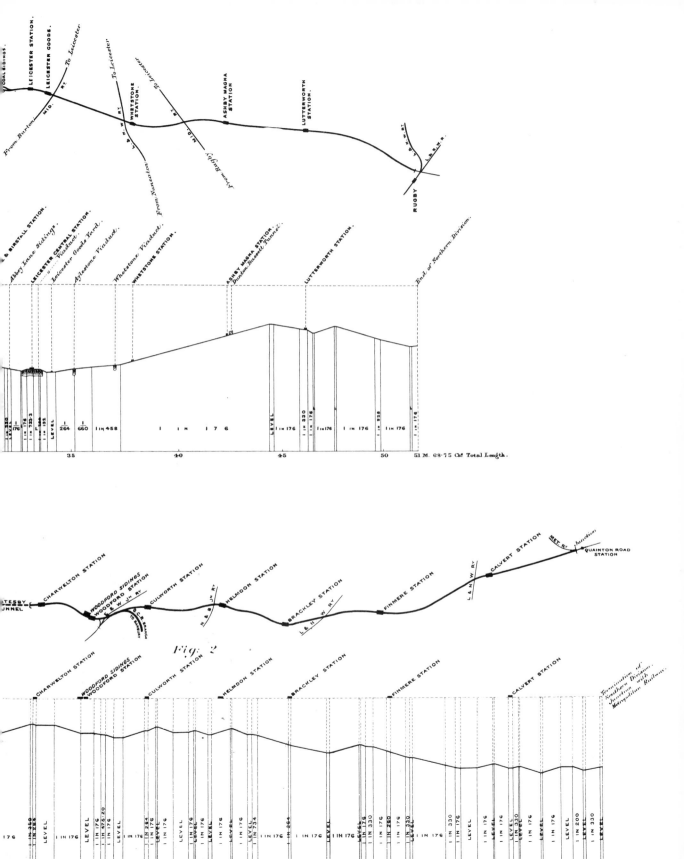

COAL SIDINGS.
LEICESTER STATION.
LEICESTER GOODS.
To Leicester
From Burton **MID. RY.**
WHETSTONE STATION.
To Leicester
To Leicester
G. & N. W. RY.
ASHBY MAGNA STATION.
MID.
From Rugby
LUTTERWORTH STATION.
From Nuneaton
G. & N. W. RY.
L. & N. W. R.
RUGBY.

& BIRSTALL STATION.
Abbey Lane Sidings.
LEICESTER CENTRAL STATION.
Viaduct.
Leicester Goods Yard.
Aylestone Viaduct.
Whetstone Viaduct.
WHETSTONE STATION.
ASHBY MAGNA STATION.
Dunton Bassett Tunnel.
LUTTERWORTH STATION.
End of Northern Division.

| 1 IN 330 | LEVEL | 1 IN 176 | 1 IN 792·3 | L 1 IN 594 | 1 IN 192 | LEVEL | 1 264 | 1 660 | 1 IN 458 | 1 IN 176 | LEVEL | 1 IN 330 | 1 IN 176 | 1 IN 176 | 1 IN 176 | 1 IN 936 | 1 IN 176 |

35   40   45   50   **51 M. 68·75 Chs Total Length.**

CHARWELTON STATION.
WOODFORD SIDINGS
WOODFORD STATION.
L. & N. W. JN. RY.
To Banbury
O. C. R. BRANCH.
CULWORTH STATION.
N. & B. JN. RY.
HELMDON STATION.
BRACKLEY STATION.
L. & N. W. RY.
FINMERE STATION.
L. & N. W. RY.
CALVERT STATION.
MET. RY.
Junction
QUAINTON ROAD STATION.
TESSBY
UNNEL

Fig. 2

CHARWELTON STATION.
WOODFORD SIDINGS
WOODFORD STATION.
CULWORTH STATION.
HELMDON STATION.
BRACKLEY STATION.
FINMERE STATION.
CALVERT STATION.
Termination of Southern Division. Junction with Metropolitan Railway.

| 176 | 1 IN 360 | LEVEL | LEVEL | 1 IN 176 | 1 IN 475·20 | 1 IN 176 | LEVEL | 1 IN 264 | LEVEL | 1 IN 176 | LEVEL | 1 IN 176 | 1 IN 176 | LEVEL | LEVEL | 1 IN 176 | 1 IN 734 | LEVEL | 1 IN 264 | LEVEL | 1 IN 176 | LEVEL | 1 IN 330 | 1 IN 176 | 1 IN 260 | LEVEL | 1 IN 330 | LEVEL | 1 IN 176 | 1 IN 176 | 1 IN 330 | LEVEL | LEVEL | 1 IN 176 | LEVEL | 1 IN 330 | LEVEL | 1 IN 176 | 1 IN 176 | LEVEL | 1 IN 176 | 1 IN 200 | 1 IN 330 | LEVEL |

135   140   145   150   155   160   **161 Miles 49·4 Chains**

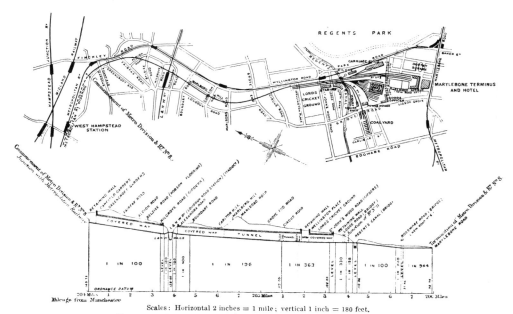

Scales: Horizontal 2 inches = 1 mile; vertical 1 inch = 180 feet.

PLAN AND LONGITUDINAL SECTION OF THE METROPOLITAN DIVISION.

Introduction

The terminus of the Great Central Railway at Marylebone has been aptly described as a gentleman's station. One of the smallest of London's termini and the last to be built, it never knew the jostling crowds and the frenetic clamour such as pervades the other, larger London stations, particularly those serving the south. There was never any 'rush hour' worthy of the name at Marylebone and no one ever seemed to be in a hurry. Standing in its quiet, spacious concourse, cut off from the fretful sound of the traffic in the Marylebone Road by the huge bulk of the Great Central Hotel across the forecourt, you half expected to hear the sound of cathedral bells. Even the arrival or departure of its not-too-frequent trains scarcely disturbed this atmosphere of cloistered calm. Marylebone trains, like its station staff, seemed to go about their business with less self-assertion and fuss than those of other London stations. The peace of Marylebone boded ill for Great Central shareholders, but it certainly made things very pleasant for the railway's patrons, making them feel as though they were members of some exclusive club.

Before the great British railway companies lost their separate identities, their London termini, in some intangible way, had become redolent of the territories they served. Once under Brunel's great roof at Paddington you felt that you were already halfway to the West Country; Liverpool Street seemed essentially East Anglian and what could have spoken more eloquently of Pennine moors and mills than that great propylœum of blackened stone at Euston? Although it was such a latecomer, the same could be said for Marylebone. Its rails led ultimately to the black north also, and yet for me its quietness always recalled vividly to mind that 'slumbering Midland plain' to which it was the gateway, an empty quarter lying behind the eyes of its signal lamps.

Apart from marching defiantly before the walls of the London and North Western citadel of Rugby, the main line of the Great Central touches no urban centre of importance between Marylebone and Leicester, so the words 'empty quarter' are no empty figure of speech. Although I seldom had occasion to use the railway, I came to know this region well in my canal boating days, for the heart of it is that high wold country that occupies the borders of Northamptonshire, Oxfordshire and Warwickshire, stretching north-east into Leicestershire. It is a land bordered on the west and north by the Oxford Canal and on the east by the Grand Union. I can still hear that rapid, rhythmical hollow thunder of wheels, suddenly breaking into the silence of slow journeys as a north-bound Great Central express, tearing down the long bank from Charwelton summit tunnel, crossed the girder bridge over the Oxford Canal near Braunston. It is a sound that will be heard no more.

Tilted pastures with narrow roads, unfenced and gated, meandering across them to small hill-top villages of golden stone, this is the country I associate with the Great Central. Because it forms the central watershed of England, here the rivers Cherwell, Leam, Ouse and Nene have their sources. The rain that falls upon these wolds may find its way into any one of a dozen winding, willow-bordered streams and so be borne away to the Nore, to the Bristol Channel or to the Wash. It is a country that gives the lie to those who suppose that the Midlands of England are now no more than a vast built-up area. Windy upland meadows corrugated with ancient ridge and furrow and deserted villages like Wolfhamcote bear silent witness to the fact that in many areas it was more populous in the Middle Ages than it is today. Small wonder that it was still a vacant space on the railway map of the early 1890s. Only a few minor cross-country lines snaked their tortuous way across it from east to west.

Yet it was this vacant territory that the engineers of the Great Central chose to occupy when they drove England's last main line southwards towards London. Indeed, so closely do the routes of the Great Western, London and North Western, Midland and Great Northern converge as they approach the metropolis that the newcomers really had no alternative but to choose this difficult and sparsely populated corridor for their new railway.

The challenge was magnificently taken. Despite the fact that they drove their line across the grain of the country and along the very spine of the watershed, there is no gradient steeper than 1 in 176, no curve of less than one mile radius. To maintain such exacting standards involved extremely heavy engineering works; a succession of deep cuttings alternating with lofty embankments and such major structural undertakings as the 2,997-yd Catesby tunnel and a great 23-span viaduct across the valley of the infant Ouse at Brackley.

In breadth of conception and boldness of execution this 'London Extension', as it was called, bore a closer resemblance to Robert Stephenson's London and Birmingham, Brunel's Great Western or Locke's London and Southampton lines built in the first heroic age of railway construction fifty years before, than to any of the lines built subsequently. Begun in 1894 and opened for passenger traffic in 1899, it was destined to be the last grand gesture of a century that had given birth to railways. Commercially it was foredoomed to failure; the last to come, it was the first to go. While it was being built, the first hesitant 'horseless carriages' appeared on the English roads. Few took them seriously; fewer still foresaw that in a few years so ridiculous and crude a vehicle would bring the proud railways to their knees. In this sense, the Great Central was an anachronism from the day it was built, but this in no way detracts from its splendour as an engineering achievement.

In the building of the Great Central, railway history was repeating itself. In 1862, an enterprising and thriving provincial railway company, whose trains could only reach the capital by means of unsatisfactory running powers over other companies' metals, had resolved to build its own line to London. The result was the Midland Railway extension to St Pancras. Thirty years later, another provincial railway, the Manchester, Sheffield and Lincolnshire, also sought and obtained powers to extend its metals to London. Thinking its name ill-suited to the dignity of this new trunk line, it changed it to Great Central while the London Extension was still in the making.

In their standing at the time they made their costly bids for the capital, however, the two companies were poles apart. Although it was then a provincial company based on Derby, the Midland was already the fourth largest railway in the kingdom with 687 route miles of line and a further 80 miles under construction. Moreover, thanks to the wise guidance of its great Chairman, John Ellis, and the brilliant management of James Allport, the Midland's financial position was second to none. Its stock stood higher than that of any other railway company in Britain and paid a steady 6 per cent on the ordinary shares. Finally, it should be remembered that in 1862, when the Midland made its momentous decision, the railways of this country were in the high noon of their prosperity. By contrast, although the MS&L owned a sizeable system by 1892, it was certainly not a prosperous concern. It had never paid more than 3½ per cent on its ordinary shares since it had been incorporated in 1846 and for nine years it was in default. Small wonder that wags alleged that its initials stood for 'Money Sunk and Lost'. Why then should this impoverished company have embarked on a costly scheme for a London Extension which a distinguished economic historian★ described as 'a belated and almost entirely superfluous product of the original era of fighting construction'? The answer lies in the ambition of one man – Sir Edward Watkin, Chairman of the MS&L since 1864.

If the Extension scheme was an anachronism, so was its author. The son of a Manchester cotton merchant, Sir Edward Watkin was a man of the same calibre as George Hudson, the famous – or infamous – 'Railway King'. The turbulent railway world of the 1840s in which Hudson had his being would have been Watkin's true element, but in the more staid world of the 1880s and '90s he was an isolated phenomenon, a kind of elderly *enfant terrible* who set everybody speculating what he would be up to next. Besides the MS&L, Watkin's railway empire included London's Metropolitan Railway, the East London Railway which, by acquiring and adapting Sir Marc Brunel's famous Thames Tunnel, had formed a rail link beneath London River and, lastly, the South Eastern Railway with a main line extending from London to Dover via Folkestone. In 1881, Watkin had promoted the Submarine Continental Railway with a capital of £250,000 to prosecute a Channel Tunnel. His ambitious plan for this tunnel was worthy of the Brunels and although it failed, at least it can be said that he pushed the scheme further than anyone else had ever done, before. It is typical of Watkin that he once entertained a group of distinguished visitors to a champagne party in a special chamber hollowed out of the chalk through which the pilot tunnel was being driven beneath the Channel. One is irresistibly reminded of that earlier entertainment organized by I.K. Brunel in the uncompleted Thames Tunnel more than half a century before.

Watkin's grandiose master-plan now becomes clear. When he conceived the London Extension his sights were ranged on Europe. London was to be merely an intermediate stopping point on a great through railway route between the industrial north of England and the capitals of Europe via the Thames and Channel Tunnels. Granted this magnificent dream, it becomes easy to understand why the last main line was engineered in the old grand manner and why its stations were designed with the future quadrupling of its tracks in mind.

As craftily and methodically as any chess player, Watkin initiated the preliminary moves towards the ultimate realization of his dream. The MS&L metals were extended southwards from Beighton, near Sheffield, to Annesley, nine miles to the north of Nottingham, where they joined the Great Northern's Leen Valley line over which, by means of running powers, MS&L trains gained access to Nottingham. Meanwhile, in the south, the Metropolitan Railway,

★ Sir John Clapham quoted by George Dow in *Great Central*, Vol. 2, p. 221.

regardless of its title, was being progressively extended northwards through what was then still the heart of rural Buckinghamshire. By 1892, the same year in which the MS&L line to Annesley was completed, the Metropolitan reached Aylesbury where it made an end-on junction with the little Aylesbury and Buckingham Railway. This line was a satellite of the Metropolitan and thus a hitherto insignificant part of Watkin's empire. It connected Aylesbury with the L&NWR's Cambridge–Oxford line at Verney Junction, gaining access to Buckingham by means of running powers over the L&NWR branch line from Verney Junction to Buckingham and Banbury. As soon as the union had been effected, it became part of the Metropolitan so that, as a result of Watkin's strategy, Verney, that remote rural junction standing in fields far from any village, became the incongruous northern outpost of London's Metropolitan Railway.

Having thus set up the board, Watkin now made his master move to the consternation of his rivals in the railway world. It was a tripartite plan which provided for, first and most importantly, an entirely new main line of railway 92 miles long from Annesley, through Nottingham, Leicester and Rugby to a junction with the Aylesbury–Verney Junction line a little to the north of Quainton Road station; secondly, the widening of the Metropolitan between Willesden Green and Finchley Road, and thirdly a short new line from that company's West Hampstead station to a new London terminus at Boscobel Gardens, Marylebone.

Although he had resigned before the work actually commenced, the survey for the new railway was carried out by the company's engineer, Charles Liddell, with the help of two assistants, and the parliamentary plans and estimates prepared in time for a Bill to be presented to Parliament in 1891. It was clear that it was going to be a difficult and costly line to build. In addition to the natural obstacles already alluded to, it would have to be driven through the heart of Nottingham, Leicester and north London. The problem of carrying a new line of way through dense urban areas is one familiar to our modern builders of motorways and inner ring roads, but it was then novel in its magnitude. Earlier engineers had encountered it only on a reduced scale because it had largely been railways which had caused the subsequent urban growth.

When the Bill for the London Extension came before Parliament it encountered bitter opposition. Not surprisingly, it was opposed by both the Great Northern and the Midland Railway Companies, but these two giants were joined by many other objectors ranging from local authorities to artists and cricketers. The artists' colony in St John's Wood, headed by Alma Tadema, protested vigorously against the crude violation of their select suburb while, at the bidding of the MCC, the cricketers of the country rose as one man to defend the sacred turf of Lords against the company's threat to undermine it. The Bill was thrown out but, spurred on by the indomitable Watkin, the company would not accept defeat and resolved to fight again.

The two rival railway companies had argued logically that their existing lines between London and the north-east Midlands were perfectly adequate for the traffic offering and that a third route would be completely superfluous. Sir Edward Watkin countered this by maintaining that the growth of traffic would soon compel these companies to widen and improve their lines. Rather than what he termed the 'plastering up' of these old lines, it would be better to build a completely new one. Sir Edward did not recognize the 'horseless carriage' as a powerful enemy at the railways' gates and, strange though it may seem to us now, neither did Parliament for this argument was accepted and at the second attempt the MS&L got its Bill. In an age of technological change, it is unwise to assume that present trends will continue into the foreseeable future and his shareholders would pay dearly for Watkin's stubborn faith in railways.

In this second Bill, the irate artists were to some extent soothed by the decision to abandon Boscobel Gardens as a location for the new terminus in favour of a more central site fronting the Marylebone Road. The militant cricketers were placated by an undertaking to 'cut and cover' the new line where it passed under the corner of Lords cricket ground, subsequently restoring the turf to pristine condition. The company also agreed to extend the ground over the site of some demolished property, a handsome *douceur* which cost the MS&L the best part of £40,000. It was in this revised form that the London Extension Bill, after a protracted struggle, finally received the Royal Assent at the end of March 1893.

Some little time then elapsed while the contract drawings and sections were prepared and while the impoverished company made frantic efforts to raise the necessary capital. The work was divided into seven contracts and these money-raising efforts were so rewarded that by September 1894 all seven had been let for a total sum of £3,182,155 and the six contractors moved in with a force of 9,450 men at their back. Although the use of steam-driven mechanical plant reduced the total number of horses to a mere 290, railway construction still demanded considerable manpower. The actual cost of the work, including compensation and the amount spent in building houses to replace those demolished, finally totalled over £11½ million. This meant that construction was only kept going by continued money-raising efforts. In retrospect, it is remarkable that these efforts were so successful.

But that this was by no means the end of the story was at least partly due to the waning influence of Sir Edward Watkin. He was seventy-four years of age by the time the London Extension Bill became law. The old buccaneer's fighting spirit could no longer stand the strain after a long lifetime of belligerent railway politics and, shortly afterwards, he retired from the chairmanship of his companies. Although he remained on their Boards, lacking the cement of his dynamic leadership, disagreements broke out, his railway empire began to crumble and his dream to fade. In railway circles it was confidently predicted that his resignation signalled the death of the London Extension, but this was not so. Although Watkin's dream was never to be realized, such was the impetus his personality had imparted that the London Extension went forward to completion.

That it did not take the form he had originally envisaged, but was orientated in a somewhat different direction, was due to the bickering which broke out between the Boards of the Great Central (to give the MS&L its new title) and the Metropolitan Railways soon after Watkin relinquished control. Only one source of dispute need concern us here. This was the refusal, except under intolerable conditions, of the Metropolitan to permit the Great Central to use its connections with the District Line (the Inner Circle) at Baker Street for the through working of goods traffic on to the South Eastern Railway via the Thames Tunnel. Faced with this impasse, the Great Central had no alternative but to look for some other outlet for through traffic to the south. It looked westward to the Great Western Railway which agreed to loan the money to enable the Great Central to build a new railway 8½ miles long, to connect its own main line at Woodford with the GWR's Oxford–Birmingham line at Banbury. This line, authorized in 1896 and completed in 1900, continued to handle a very considerable interchange traffic until the 1950s when it fell victim to the Beeching 'axe'. Nor was it the only issue of the alliance between the two companies.

In one respect, Sir Edward Watkin's visionary scheme had been gravely at fault. He had not grasped the truism that the strength of a chain is its weakest link. Although the London Extension was laid out in a manner worthy of the pioneers, the same could not be said for the Metropolitan extension over the Chilterns to Aylesbury upon which access to London depended. Its steep gradients and sharp curvature made it unsuitable both for fast express running and for heavy goods traffic. Severe speed restrictions had to be imposed and it soon became apparent that the money spent in making the London Extension a locomotive 'galloping ground' had been very largely wasted. Furthermore, as a result of vigorous advertising on the part of the Metropolitan which popularized this Buckinghamshire 'Metroland' as highly desirable commuter territory, its Aylesbury line became cluttered with a growing volume of suburban traffic through which it became increasingly difficult for Great Central long-distance traffic to find paths. This circumstance combined with Metropolitan intransigence to induce the Great Central to seek some alternative route into London.

In the summer of 1897, the GWR obtained powers to construct a new line over the Chilterns from its main line at Old Oak Common to High Wycombe where it would join the existing GWR branch line from Maidenhead to the Wycombes and Princes Risborough where it divided to serve Thame and Aylesbury. It was in this project that the Great Central saw its salvation and it promptly sought powers to build a connecting line from Neasden to join this new railway at Northolt. The Act for this railway was passed in 1898 in the teeth of fierce opposition from the Metropolitan. The two companies next set up a Joint Committee to build the already authorized GWR. line from Northolt to High Wycombe, to double and re-align the old branch line between High Wycombe and Princes Risborough and to extend a new joint line thence to a junction with the Great Central's London Extension at Grendon Underwood, two miles north of Quainton Road. Contractors for this new joint undertaking were Pauling & Company, Northolt to High Wycombe, and Mackay & Davies of Cardiff who undertook the remainder.

So far as the GWR was concerned, this new joint line had first been promoted as part of that company's projected direct route to Birmingham. The second phase of this scheme was the construction of a new railway from a junction with the joint line at Ashendon to Aynho where it joined the company's old route to Birmingham via Oxford. It was one of an ambitious series of new 'cut-offs' built by the GWR at this time which helped to invalidate the old slur that its initials stood for 'Great Way Round'. When it was completed, that portion of the joint line between Ashendon and Grendon Underwood reverted by mutual agreement to the sole ownership of the Great Central.

It was thus in the interests of both companies that their new joint line should be laid out with gradients and curvature suitable for express running. So, although it was four and a half miles longer than the Metropolitan route, this, combined with the fact that it was generally less congested, made it a very useful alternative route where the Great Central was concerned.

After the London Extension had been opened for passenger traffic in 1899, all Great Central trains used the Metropolitan route until November 1905 when the new joint line was opened for goods traffic. Passenger trains began using it a year later. By this time, relations between the Great Central and the Metropolitan had improved. Consequently, throughout the lifetime of the London Extension, its traffic continued to use both routes into London depending on the traffic paths available.

When the Great Central lost its identity by becoming a constituent of the London and North Eastern Railway, goods and passenger services over the London Extension continued much as before, but when Britain's railways were nationalized it soon became obvious that the future of a main line which had never proved economically viable was in grave doubt. The 'Master Cutler' express that ran once a day each way between Sheffield and Marylebone was destined to be the last of the many fine trains that have used the London Extension. Today this railway lies derelict, its vacant, weed-grown road-bed a forlorn monument to the *folie de grandeur* of Sir Edward Watkin. But while we deplore the folly of his decision, we cannot but admire the splendid engineering which that decision called forth.

By the 1890s the average Victorian had become somewhat blasé about new railway construction. After all, he could hardly be expected to go on lauding the feats of the railway builders indefinitely. For a modern parallel, one has only to contrast the amount of interest and publicity which the construction and opening of our first motorway, the M1, attracted with the small attention that similar projects receive today. So, but for two circumstances, one of them purely fortuitous, we might know little about the building of England's last main line or what manner of men they were who built it. Posterity may well wonder what hands raised and rivetted those steel spans, drove that tunnel through the lias at Charwelton or reared the piers and turned the arches of those towering viaducts.

If the public was apathetic about the building of the London Extension, the engineers were not. Because many years had passed since any railway work of comparable magnitude had been undertaken, they were anxious to learn details about it and to know how much the state of the art had developed. Their curiosity was satisfied by no less than three papers covering the Northern, Southern and Metropolitan Divisons of the new railway which were presented to the Institution of Civil Engineers by Frederick Bidder, Francis Fox and Messrs George Hobson and Edmund Wragge respectively. Together with the lengthy discussions which followed them, they were printed in the Institution's *Proceedings* for 1900 and 1901. Together they constitute a mine of information from which all the facts in this book have been quarried and I am happy to acknowledge my indebtedness to the Institution of Civil Engineers.

Fully detailed and illustrated with numerous engineering drawings and diagrams, these three papers present all the information about the building of the railway that a civil engineer could require. But they do not stir the imagination of the layman because they do not enable him to visualize what a work of such magnitude really looked like while it was going on. To do this they need to be accompanied by photographs, not diagrams, a need that was providentially supplied by Mr S.W.A. Newton.

As a young man, Newton had joined the family photographic business in Leicester shortly before work on the London Extension began. Wholly captivated by the sheer magnitude and variety of this undertaking, he began making a photographic record of it. Judging from the number of photographs he took, his interest became almost obsessive. Travelling by train and bicycle, he covered the whole length of the new line from Annesley to Marylebone. And as if this were not enough he subsequently also covered the construction of the joint line from Northolt as far as Princes Risborough. We must be thankful that the photographic business was evidently so indulgent, for such an exercise must have taken up a prodigious amount of his time, not to mention a lavish use of photographic materials.

The end product of Newton's single-minded enthusiasm was over 2,000 glass-plate negatives – the most comprehensive and evocative record we have of the art of railway construction at the end of the Victorian age. Newton did for the Great Central what J.C. Bourne had done for Stephenson's London and Birmingham and Brunel's Great Western in the distant dawn of the railway age. It may seem impious to bracket Newton's pictures with Bourne's incomparable lithographs, but whereas an artist's work is necessarily a highly personal interpretation of things seen, the cool, objective eye of the camera records an undistorted image of the past, a window of clear glass through which we are privileged to peer into the past, saying to ourselves confidently: 'This is how it really was.' Hence the documentary value and fascination of old photographs.

Shortly before he died in 1960, S.W.A. Newton presented his collection of negatives to the Leicester City Museum and Art Gallery. Some have subsequently been reproduced in Museum publications while others have been used as illustrations in such books as George Dow's monumental three volume history *Great Central* or Terry Coleman's *The Railway Navvies*, but these represent only a minute fraction of the total. So it was decided to publish a more comprehensive selection of Newton's photographs and this book is the result.

To make a representative and meaningful choice from such a largesse of material in such a way that the story of construction is told through the eye of Newton's camera has not been easy. He could not be omniscient, while it is clear that some aspects of his subject attracted him more than others; hence the varying length of the following sections. Again, the captions given to the pictures by the photographer are sometimes sketchy and sometimes non-existent. This has called for a lot of detective work in which I have been greatly helped by Mr T.A. Walden and his staff of the Leicester City Museum and by numerous others. I would particularly like to acknowledge the expert assistance of Mr T.W. Broughton of Ruston–Bucyrus Limited, Lincoln, who identified, and supplied details of, some of the early steam excavators.

Such is the unique quality and value of the Newton Collection that I felt honoured and delighted when I was asked if I would make this selection from it and write an accompanying text. It has been an enthralling task and now I can only hope that others may derive as much pleasure from this book as I had in making it.

L.T.C.R.

1 The Way and Works

Administratively, the new line of railway was divided into three parts: a Northern Divison from Annesley Junction to Rugby, a distance of 51 miles 69 chains, a Southern Division, 40 miles 5.4 chains long from Rugby to Quainton Road, and a Metropolitan Division which covered the new London terminus at Marylebone and the short but crucial and difficult new line, just under two miles long, linking this new station with the widened line of the Metropolitan Railway by an end-on junction at Canfield Gardens, Hampstead. Edward Parry was engineer in charge of the Northern Divison, while Sir Douglas Fox and Francis Fox shared the responsibility for the Southern and Metropolitan Divisions.

For contract purposes, the line was divided into seven sections as follows:

Section	Length	Contractor
1. Annesley–Leake	19m. 44ch.	Logan & Hemmingway
2. Leake–Aylestone	16m. 36ch.	Henry Lovatt
3. Aylestone–Rugby	15m. 69ch.	Topham, Jones & Railton
4. Rugby–Charwelton★	15m. 77ch.	T. Oliver & Son
5. Charwelton★–Brackley	12m. 32ch.	Walter Scott & Company
6. Brackley–Quainton Road	12m. 61ch.	Walter Scott & Company
7. Canfield Gardens–Marylebone†	1m. 71ch.	J. T. Firbank

★ Subsequently altered to Woodford, south end.
† This section was simply referred to the Metropolitan Division.

As the following pictures show, the commencement of construction in November 1894 brought scenes of destruction and apparent chaos to town and country alike which are comparable to modern motorway works. Swathes were cut through woodlands; crudely laid construction lines invaded the countryside and the inhabitants of hitherto remote cottages and farmsteads found their privacy rudely interrupted. From their windows they looked out on a wilderness of raw earth teeming with men and machines. In Nottingham and Leicester, property was demolished wholesale to clear a path for the new railway. The company had to erect no less than 300 new houses to replace those demolished in clearing the site for Nottingham Victoria station alone. Yet work proceeded with surprising speed and order was very soon restored.

To build a railway of such easy gradient and generous curvature across the grain of the English Midlands involved extremely heavy earthworks, over twelve million cubic yards of spoil being excavated on the Northern and Southern Divisions. To avoid slips in deep cuttings or on lofty embankments, great care was taken to ensure adequate drainage. Field drains were intercepted before cuttings were commenced and, when forming embankments, the land beneath them was thoroughly drained by similar means before tipping was begun.

The formation width in cuttings was 29 ft and on embankments 31 ft although the latter figure was sometimes increased to 33 ft because the amount of spoil excavated generally exceeded that required for the embankments. As the photographs show, both end tipping and side tipping methods were used in forming the embankments. Of these, end tipping was the traditional English method and the use of side tipping provoked some controversy among engineers who argued that the method did not allow the spoil to be sufficiently compacted. However, for obvious reasons, side tipping was the quicker method and its judicious use on the Great Central undoubtedly speeded up the work and was not followed by any disastrous slips, although it was occasionally necessary to secure the embankment foot by a retaining wall. The usual method adopted was to raise the core of the bank by the traditional method of end tipping and subsequently to widen it by side tipping.

One notable embankment containing 486,000 cu yd of spoil may be taken as an example. Situated near Sulgrave, it is 43 ft high and, with slopes of 1 in 3, is 340 ft wide at the base, covering a land area of 17 acres.

ABOVE & CENTRE
The way through the woods, Wilton Park
BELOW
Rugby: A contractor's railway switchbacks along the line of route

21

TOP
Lutterworth: The site for the station
CENTRE
Brackley: The approach to the station
BELOW
Near Hucknall Torkard, Notts.

LEFT
Bricklayers at work, probably in Leicester
CENTRE
Nottingham: Off Lower Parliament Street, looking
north
BELOW LEFT & RIGHT
Through the heart of Nottingham: (left) the site of
Victoria station and (right) Parliament Street

TOP LEFT & RIGHT
Leicester: Talbot Lane and Bath Lane
ABOVE LEFT & RIGHT
Clearing the site for Leicester Central Station
LEFT
In St John's Wood
BELOW LEFT
Near Marylebone

LEFT
Engine *Aberdeen* tipping near Rothley Brook
ABOVE
Blackbird Lane, Leicester

ABOVE
The top of the tip: near Swithland, Leics.
LEFT
Side tipping on an embankment between Northolt and Harrow

BELOW LEFT
Earth cutting on the site of Bulwell Forest station.
Notice the crude stub points of the contractor's line
BOTTOM LEFT
Rock cutting for the branch line to Mountsorrel
Quarries, Leics.
BELOW RIGHT
A contractor's traffic signal beside a temporary road
bridge spanning a cutting. Shawell to Churchover
Road, Leicester

2 Raw Materials and Depots

The six main contractors for the seven contracts soon established depots at strategic points along the line of route for the storage of plant and for the handling and preparation of the raw materials used in construction. The decision to use brickwork, set in lime or cement mortar, wherever possible, for bridges in preference to stone or steel led to an immense demand for these materials. All such structures were faced with Staffordshire brindle bricks which had to be imported, as were the specially moulded Staffordshire blue bricks used for copings, but many of the common bricks used were fired locally. For example, Walter Scott & Company laid down a large brick-making plant at Great Covert Wood, near Sulgrave, covering 7 acres, where twelve million bricks were produced during the 36 months of construction.

Stone was used only for such things as girder-beds, arch-springers, newell and pilaster caps. These were of Derbyshire gritstone produced in a mason's yard on the Northern Divison between Bulwell and Hucknall Torkard. Much of the lime used for mortar was burnt in kilns constructed on site, but there was an acute shortage of suitable sand and gravel for concrete making. Only one suitable pocket was found when excavating a cutting near Calvert, but for the most part burnt clay ballast was used in place of gravel, while most of the sand used on the Southern Division was drawn from Leighton Buzzard.

Of the contractors' depots illustrated in the following pictures, that of Walter Scott at Helmdon is of particular interest. For convenience of access to the Northampton and Banbury branch line to Banbury which runs along the valley at this point, the depot was sited beneath the piers of the new Helmdon Viaduct, one of which can be seen building in the left foreground of the picture. This meant that the contractor's railway from the depot to the level of the line of route was extremely steeply graded, the maximum grade being 1 in 9 on a 5-chain curve. Nevertheless, the engineer for the section reported that one locomotive could comfortably take up two loaded main line wagons weighing 23 tons, while under the most favourable conditions a total of 75 tons had ascended this formidable incline. The contractor's locomotives storming up this bank must have been a spectacular sight and it is a pity that it escaped the eagle eye of Newton's camera.

OPPOSITE
Straight and true: The new formation looking north from East Leake Tunnel, Notts.

ABOVE
Brickworks at Great Covert Wood, Sulgrave, Northants.
FAR LEFT
Clay for the brickmakers
LEFT
Contractor's branch line from Whetstone to Narborough Brickworks, Leics.
BELOW, FAR LEFT
A line-side lime kiln south of East Leake Tunnel, Notts.
BELOW LEFT
Stonemason's yard near Bulwell, Notts.
BOTTOM
A seam of sand discovered in the cutting at Birstall proved to be a lucky find for the contractor

30

Henry Lovatt's depot at Loughborough

LEFT
Walter Scott's depot at Helmdon, Northants.
BELOW
Carpenters' shop in J.T. Firbank's yard, Alpha Road,
London Division

LEFT
GWR engineer's office on the joint line
BELOW
Section engineer's site office, interior, Claydon, Bucks.

3 *Mechanical Plant*

The days when railways were built entirely by the muscle power of men and horses were definitely over by the time construction of the Great Central began. The British navvy had fought his last epic and unaided battle on the moorlands of the high Pennines when he drove the Midland main line from Settle to Carlisle. For very soon after this battle had been won Joseph Ruston introduced his famous 'Steam Navvy' which was first used in the construction of the Midland line from Melton Mowbray to Nottingham in 1880. It at once reduced the cost of excavation from 14d. per cubic yard to 2½d. or 1½d. depending on the nature of the ground.

Of the formidable array of steam plant mustered by the men who built the Great Central, steam navvies were, so to speak, the heavy artillery and no less than forty-three of these monsters were employed throughout the line. They proved capable of digging their way through rock provided it was judiciously loosened beforehand by blasting, but in some cases where the going proved particularly slow and difficult they worked day and night by the aid of 'Lucigen' lights. The overwhelming majority of these excavators were Rustons, but there were rare exceptions, two of which Newton captured with his camera. The makers of these machines seem to have assumed that the rugged men who would operate them needed no protection of any kind from the weather. Consequently the first thing the contractors did was to build crude shelters on them out of timber and corrugated iron which resembled shepherds' huts. These improvised shelters gave the steam navvy a curiously ramshackle and endearing appearance, effectually disguising a formidable and beautifully maintained machine.

Twenty-one steam cranes were used on the Northern Division. The number employed on the Southern Division was not recorded but was probably about the same. They were extensively employed in bridge building, lifting steel girder sections or bricks and mortar by the bucketful for the use of bricklayers working on the high viaducts. Like the excavators, they were provided with no shelter for their drivers and were often fitted with extempore cabs.

No less than fifty-three portable steam engines of the standard agricultural type were employed on the Northern Division alone. They were used to drive mortar mills and to power the pumps that lifted water out of the sumps to which the temporary drainage systems led.

The contractors' locomotives, ninety-four in all, were the ubiquitous and indispensable work-horses of the whole job, chivvying nearly 4,000 wagons over 200 miles of temporary tracks. Beautifully maintained by their proud drivers they gleamed with lustrous paintwork and highly polished metal. Their immaculate appearance was all the more praiseworthy because they worked under most adverse conditions. They were frequently stabled in the open. They had to run over appallingly rough and muddy tracks and, to assist them in this respect, many were fitted with compensated springs and an arrangement of pipes which enabled their wheel tyres to be cleaned with water drawn from their tanks. Nearly all of them were built by the three Leeds firms which succeeded E.B. Wilson's famous Railway Foundry, namely Manning Wardle, Hudswell Clarke and the Hunslet Engine Company. Many were new, but some were veterans which had seen service on earlier railway building contracts. The sight of these smart little locomotives and the contrast they made with the crude contractors' wagons they hauled around obviously captivated Newton for he took a great number of pictures of them of which it is only possible to reproduce a small selection here. For further photographs and more information about the history of these engines and their technical details, the reader is referred to *Contractors' Locomotives, G.C.R.* by Neil Cossons, BA, published by Leicester Museums, which is now, unfortunately, out of print.

A Ruston excavator at work near Wembley Park. In
the background can be seen the first stage of the great
steel tower to be built by the Metropolitan Tower
Company, an abortive project with which Sir Edward
Watkin was associated. Its 300-ft legs straddled
121 acres. It was intended to be 700 ft high but never
got beyond this first stage

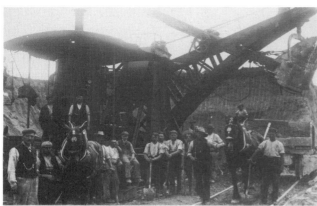

ABOVE LEFT & RIGHT
Excavators at work on unrecorded locations
FAR LEFT & BOTTOM
Excavators in action near Brackley and in the centre
of Nottingham
LEFT
Excavator working near the Regent's Canal crossing,
Marylebone

ABOVE LEFT
Day's work done: an excavator 'resting'
ABOVE RIGHT
Excavator working south of Birstall Pit Lane,
Leicester
BELOW
A new Ruston excavator without cabin showing
boiler, engine and control gear

ABOVE

Two rarities. Right: Crane Navvy with steam thrust cylinder in the bucket arm built by John H. Wilson of Liverpool as used in the building of the Manchester Ship Canal. Left: Crane Navvy by Whitaker & Sons of Leeds. It had steam-powered racking gear consisting of a steam cylinder supported in trunnions in the jib, the piston rod being directly connected to cranks to provide a measure of control of depth of cut through the bucket arms. Both machines were adaptations of steam crane designs built *c.* 1887

RIGHT

Steam crane with cab fitted, Goldhurst Terrace, West Hampstead

BELOW

Steam crane lifting steel bridge sections, Nottingham

ABOVE LEFT
A wayside temporary pumping installation utilizing a portable steam engine near Rugby
ABOVE RIGHT
A small steam pump. Even this small item of plant was beautifully maintained
RIGHT
Steam pile-driver, Stanford on Soar, Notts.
BELOW
Presumably the foreman wasn't looking when Newton took this picture

LEFT
Messrs Topham, Jones & Railton's locomotive
stabling point at Ashby Magna
BELOW
Locomotives were the contractors' maids-of-all-work
Birstall cutting, Leicestershire

ABOVE LEFT & RIGHT
Two new Manning Wardle locomotives; left, at
Twyford, Bucks. and right, at Denham. Standing on
the right in the left-hand picture is a navvy missioner
BELOW LEFT & RIGHT
Two locomotives by Hudswell Clarke. The *Newcastle*
worked on the Walter Scott contract and was based at
Helmdon. The *Birkenhead* is seen here at Haddenham
BOTTOM LEFT & RIGHT
Two Hunslet locomotives. *Mersey* was supplied new
to T.A. Walker in 1887 for use on the Manchester
Ship Canal contract and was photographed at
Neasden. *Cliftonville* had been cut down for use in
restricted tunnel headings, and is pictured between
Alpha Road and the Regent's Canal

Two of Henry Lovatt's veteran Manning Wardles.
The elegant classical safety valve casing of No. 2 (at
Leicester) is in the old tradition of the Railway
Foundry. She was built in 1872 and originally worked
on the Settle and Carlisle Railway. No.15 was built in
1868 and was first used in the building of the
Lancashire Union Railway but is seen here at Rothley,
Leicestershire

ABOVE
An elegant little Manning Wardle side-tank
locomotive at Grendon Underwood, Bucks
BELOW LEFT
When the new joint line from Neasden to Grendon
Underwood was being built, the contractors, Pauling
& Co., used a number of the famous 'Brighton
Terriers' bought from the LB&SCR. Here is
Bishopsgate, built at Brighton in 1876
BELOW RIGHT
Manning Wardle 3-ft gauge *Lancashire Witch*, built in
1876 and used in the construction of the Brackley
Station approaches was, so far as is known, the only
narrow gauge locomotive used during the
construction of the Great Central

An engineer's inspection trolley powered by an
internal combustion engine at Denham, *c.* 1906. It
was probably built by the Drewry Car Co. Ltd of
Teddington. Who could have foretold then that the
internal combustion engine would ultimately spell the
downfall of steam power on rails?

4 *Bridges and Viaducts*

The builders of the Great Central were faced with many man-made obstacles such as the railway pioneers in the first half of the nineteenth century had never encountered. There were such things as existing main line railways to be crossed without interrupting their traffic, a new reservoir, and a canal on a high embankment, while the cities of Nottingham and Leicester had swollen to present a formidable urban barrier to the new line. Consequently, although the general engineering policy was to build bridges in brickwork wherever possible to avoid the continuing maintenance required by steel, many bridges of large span were needed and for these only steel girders would serve.

The largest brick structures were the viaducts at Leicester (over 1 mile long and up to 180 ft wide), Nottingham, Bulwell, Swithland, Willoughby, Staverton, Catesby, Helmdon and Brackley. In the case of the last four structures, in order to guard against the effect of ground movement, the pier bases were linked and strengthened by means of whole or partial inverts. The haunches between their spandrel walls were filled up with concrete and the resulting level deck sealed with five alternate layers of asphalt and canvas before the ballast was laid.

On the Northern Division, wherever there was a risk of mining subsidence, all steel girder bridges were built as two independent structures for up and down lines so that one could receive attention without interfering with the other. This policy was adopted throughout the Southern Division.

The railway passes under the northern part of Nottingham in tunnel, but then the ground dips abruptly and the line had to be carried on a continuous viaduct, 1,000 yd long, consisting of fifty-three brick arches interspersed with steel girder spans. The greatest of the latter carried the line across the western end of the Midland station by a single clear span of 171 ft. This viaduct was immediately followed by the steel bridge over the Trent which was built for four lines of way.

At Leicester, the need to span numerous city streets and no less than four crossings of the River Soar called for a similar but even longer viaduct (1,842 yd) of brick arches alternating with steel girder spans. At Rugby, too, heavy bridgeworks were needed as the River Avon, the Oxford Canal and the main line of the London and North Western Railway with its fourteen tracks had to be crossed successively. Finally, at the approach to Marylebone, fourteen tracks had to be carried on the skew over the Regent's Canal by a girder bridge over 400 ft wide and containing nearly a thousand tons of steel.

The most difficult operation of all was the crossing of the Oxford Canal at Rugby, the first work in the Southern Division. The canal at this point is on an embankment, built in 1834 as part of the improvement works carried out at that time. Three steel cylinders or caissons had to be sunk through each side of the canal embankment to support the brick piers of the viaduct. The engineers were under penalty of £20 per hour for any obstruction caused to the canal and 20s. per thousand gallons of water lost so that particular care had to be taken to ensure that this operation did not 'draw' the puddled clay lining of the canal. To this end a steel trough was constructed, 80 ft 6 in long by 8 ft clear inside width. It could be sealed at both ends by means of stop planks inserted in the 'stop grooves' provided. This was floated into position and then sunk beside the bank, the canal being completely sealed off by making dams of clay puddle from each of its four corners to the banks. Canal traffic then passed through this trough while the three caissons were sunk in free air through the embankment to natural ground level below. When this had been completed, divers dug away the puddle seals, the trough was pumped out and floated across to the opposite bank where the operation was repeated. In this way the whole job was carried out without incurring any penalty. Moreover, with true economy, when it had done its work, the steel trough was utilized on the railway as a footbridge. All the steelwork used in this viaduct was brought to the site by water and raised by steam crane from the canal bank.

In one important respect the engineers of the Great Central learnt from the mistakes of their predecessors. They resolved to eliminate that major source of hazard and delay – the level crossing. With only one exception throughout the entire route, every road, from main thoroughfares to the humblest farm access, was carried by bridges either under or over the new railway. The selection of pictures which follow illustrate only some of the highlights of bridge construction, but Newton took innumerable photographs of these minor bridges. Although these become boring by repetition, they do emphasize the magnitude of the total bridge building operation. It is somewhat ironical that because nowadays rail traffic has become concentrated on our older main lines we should still be bedevilled by a level crossing problem which the engineers of a now derelict Great Central went to such pains and expense to avoid.

Bulwell Viaduct, Notts., 400 yd long, 48 ft high,
25 arches

The Nottingham Viaduct cuts ruthlessly through the
heart of the old city. Right: Conduit Street, far right:
Waterway Street.
Bottom left: Drury Hill Passage, from Broad Marsh,
bottom right: Nottingham Viaduct from Garners Hill

ABOVE & TOP FACING PAGE
Nottingham Viaduct over the Midland Railway and
Station Road
RIGHT & BELOW
Nottingham: Trent Bridge under construction

RIGHT & BELOW
Viaduct over the Leicester Corporation reservoir at
Swithland. The reservoir was drained while it was
being built

ABOVE & LEFT
Leicester Viaduct: Columns for St Augustine's
Street Bridge
BELOW
Bridge over Soar Lane

ABOVE & BELOW
Leicester: Transporting steelwork and raising the
girders for St Augustine's Street Bridge
LEFT
Plating the bridge deck, Bath Lane, Leicester

ABOVE
Bridge over canal, Aylestone, Leics., showing
traveller used in construction
LEFT
An arched over bridge near Ashby Magna: laying
skew courses over the centring
BELOW
Aylestone Viaduct, River Soar

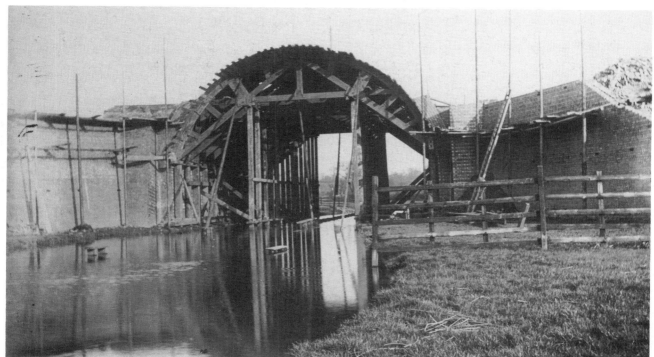

ABOVE
Centring for tunnel bridge over River Avon, Rugby
RIGHT & BELOW
Rugby: Viaduct over Oxford Canal under
construction and completed

LEFT
Bridge over Oxford Canal, Braunston & Willoughby
BELOW LEFT
Rugby: Viaduct over L&NWR On the insistence of
the L&NWR, the enormous signal gantry had to be
erected at the expense of the Great Central
RIGHT
The incomplete 'Rugby Works Viaduct' waits for the
steel spans
BELOW
Catesby Viaduct, River Leam. 476 ft long, 63 ft high,
12 arches

LEFT & ABOVE
Brackley Viaduct nearing completion over the Ouse
Valley; 755 ft long, 62 ft high, 20 arches and two
girder spans

LEFT
Laying the spandrel walls, Brackley Viaduct
BELOW
A portable engine drives a mortar mill beneath the
piers of Brackley Viaduct
RIGHT
Construction of a bridge over the Lower Icknield
Way at Longwick, Buckinghamshire

LEFT
Bridge over L&NWR at Loudoun Road, London
BELOW
Steel skew bridge over the Regent's Canal,
Marylebone

5 Tunnels

The first major tunnelling works on the new railway were driven through the high ground on which the northern part of the city of Nottingham stands. These were Sherwood Rise (662 yd) Mansfield Road (1,189 yd) and Victoria Street (392 yd). All three were driven through the bunter sandstone and in the case of the two first-named four working shafts were sunk in each, the maximum depth from the surface to rail level being 120 ft. Initially, a 12 ft square heading was driven which was large enough to allow the contractor's locomotives to pass through. The rock proved to be so solid that, except for short lengths at the tunnel entrances, only the roof was arched with brickwork, the springings being set back one foot from the face of the rock. Carrington Station was sited in the 40 ft deep rock cutting between these first two tunnels. Similarly, Nottingham Victoria Station was sited below natural ground level between the Mansfield Road and Victoria Street Tunnels.

There is little rock cover over the Victoria Street Tunnel and for a length of 100 yd under Thurland Street it was built by cut-and-cover. The rest of the tunnel was costly and difficult work. Old cellars, excavated in the rock, were broken into and the buildings above had to be carefully underpinned.

The greatest tunnelling work on the line was at Charwelton where a 3,000-yd tunnel had to be cut through the lower and middle lias of a ridge of the Northamptonshire wolds. The tunnel is straight and was driven on a continuous gradient of 1 in 176 rising towards the south. At its southern end the line attains its summit level of 503 ft above sea level. The tunnel's northern portal was situated near a large country house whose owner, not unnaturally, would not allow any working shafts to be driven within the confines of his park. This meant that for the first 500 yd the tunnel had to be driven from this northern end by means of a bottom heading and break-ups. This was unfortunate for the engineers because this portion was in the lower lias which was particularly heavy and treacherous. The greatest difficulty was experienced in keeping this heading open and on more than one occasion the 14-in square pitch-pine crown-bars broke under the pressure.

By contrast, the remaining 2,500 yd of tunnel through the lighter middle lias was constructed without difficulty and with remarkable speed. It was driven full size from nine working shafts at an average rate of 110 yd a month. The sinking of the first shaft was begun on 18 February 1895 and the last length was keyed in on 22 May 1897, an achievement which the engineers proudly claimed as a record in rapid tunnel building. Five of the working shafts were lined and left open as ventilation shafts. Four of these were 10 ft in diameter, but the diameter of the northernmost was increased to 15 ft to allow for the length which could not be ventilated.

The two miles of new line in the Metropolitan Division between the junction with the widened Metropolitan Railway at Canfield Gardens to the crossing of the Regent's Canal at the approach to Marylebone is almost entirely in tunnel, stretches of true tunnel alternating with lengths of cut-and-cover or 'covered way' as it was called. The only open sections were at the crossing over the L&NWR at Loudoun Road and a short length of 80 yd at Wellington Place before the line enters the final length of covered way under Lords Cricket Ground. In addition, however, occasional gaps were left in the roof of the covered way for purposes of ventilation.

The contractors for this division, J.T. Firbank, commenced operations by driving a 12-ft square heading throughout which allowed passage for his locomotives. The northern entrance to this tunnel section was directly below the Hampstead Baths. Here there were two portals. It was optimistically believed that four tracks would eventually be necessary and the works were laid out with this future widening in mind. Here, however, the first short length of covered way was actually built for four tracks at the outset for no very obvious reason. When the arches of the covered way had been turned, the brickwork was covered with tar before being earthed over.

At Wellington Place where the railway enters the final length of tunnel under Lords Cricket Ground over which such bitter controversy had raged, the lines begin to fan out as they approach the terminus, there being seven tracks carried in three arched ways for a distance of 213 yd beneath the ground. In fact, only a small area of land adjacent to Wellington Road was involved which in no way interfered with the cricket. On the other hand, the nearby Clergy Orphan School had to be demolished, the school being rehoused in a new building erected by the company at Bushey. When the works beneath it were completed, the old school site was laid with turf brought from Morley's Cricket Ground at Neasden which had been bought by the company to form part of its new yard. This then formed an extension to Lords, so the MCC can be said to have come very well out of the deal. Work at Lords commenced in September 1896 and was completed on 8 May of the following year.

TOP LEFT & ABOVE
South portal, Sherwood Rise Tunnel, Nottingham
LEFT
Diverting the sewers, Parliament Street, Nottingham
BELOW
South portal, Mansfield Road Tunnel, Nottingham

ABOVE LEFT
Northern portal, Victoria Street Tunnel, Nottingham
ABOVE
Southern entrance to pilot heading, Victoria Street Tunnel
LEFT & BELOW
Working shafts, Catesby Tunnel

ABOVE
Contractor's line alongside Catesby Viaduct
RIGHT
A mountain of bricks at the northern end of Catesby Tunnel
BELOW
Under the park: the northern entrance, Catesby Tunnel

LEFT & RIGHT
Catesby Tunnel, completed 1897: the northern and
southern portals
BELOW
Catesby Tunnel interior, looking south

ABOVE
Entrance to Metropolitan Tunnel section at Hampstead Baths
RIGHT
End of first tunnel section looking north from L&NWR crossing at Loudoun Road
BELOW
Looking south from L&NWR crossing to portal of second tunnel section

LEFT
Tarring the arch of the covered way off Finchley Road
BELOW
A ventilation gap in the covered way between Boundary and Marlborough Roads

ABOVE
Work in progress on the covered way, Hillgrove
Road
RIGHT
Northern entrance to final tunnel section under Lords
cricket ground
BELOW
Turning the arches of the three covered ways under
Lords

Southern entrance to the pilot heading from the Regent's Canal, Marylebone. The old St John's Wood Road Station can be seen on the right

6 Navvy Camps and Mission Halls

By the 1890s the making of a railway was not accompanied by the scenes of fierce violence, the fighting, drunkenness and debauchery such as had terrified and outraged peaceable country folk during the earlier heyday of the railway-building age. Instead of living like a savage in rude huts reminiscent of prehistoric man as he had done on the moors beside Woodhead Tunnel while a much older section of the Manchester, Sheffield and Lincolnshire Railway was being built, the navvy was now housed in hutted camps erected by the contractors. Some of these compare not unfavourably with the caravan compounds of the motorway builders of our own day.

Some camps were built beside the contractors' depots, but in order to save time in travelling to work, others were built in strategic locations along the route so that there were many more camps than there were depots. In the following pictures, Newton has recorded for us what some of these camps were like.

Although the navvy of the 1890s had become a member of a comparatively civilized species which no longer terrorized the countryside, his old reputation for lawlessness and ungodliness died hard. Judging by the number of Mission Halls which the Navvy Mission Society provided along the route, the Victorian moralists still regarded the British navvy as unregenerate, a brand to be plucked from the burning. These halls, too, Newton faithfully recorded. Looking at these pictures today with their stiff, uncomfortable benches and their pious texts nailed to bare wooden walls one can almost smell the fume of paraffin lamps and coke stoves and hear the wheezing of the harmonium. One could wish that Newton's camera had recorded the spectacle of one of these Mission Halls in full song. As it is we can only speculate how successful they were in drawing the men away from demon alcohol in the more congenial atmosphere of the nearby taproom.

LEFT & BELOW
Living-room and bedroom of a foreman's or
supervisor's family hut

TOP LEFT
A navvy foreman's hut
TOP RIGHT
Supervisors' huts and gardens at Woodford
ABOVE
Navvy camp at Woodford
BELOW
Hellidon Road Camp, Northants.

ABOVE
Leake huts above Leake Tunnel, Notts.
LEFT
Field kitchens at Quainton Road Camp
BELOW
Huts at Swithland, Leics.

Children at Newton Purcell Camp, Oxon.

ABOVE
A Northamptonshire barn in use as a Mission Reading Room
LEFT
Huts near Twyford, Bucks.
BELOW
A Mission hall in a barn at Staverton

ABOVE
Mission Hall, Loughborough
RIGHT & BELOW
Mission Room at Hucknall, Notts.

ABOVE
A casualty, Mr Birch at Catesby Navvy Mission,
3 August 1896. A rock weighing half a ton fell on his
leg in No. 7 shaft, Catesby tunnel. A collection was
made for him which raised £10
LEFT & BELOW
Interiors of Mission Rooms at Duns Lane, Leicester,
and Loughborough

TOP
The Good Samaritans Home for the Navvies,
Hucknell
RIGHT & BELOW
Mission huts at Helmdon and Catesby

If navvies wouldn't come to the Mission, the Mission
brought the Word to them

7 *The Makers*

One would have liked to include in this book pictures of some of the men responsible for the design and execution of this last main line. But, curiously enough, the engineers and the great contractors appear to have eluded Newton's otherwise omniscient camera. His collection suggests that he was much more interested in the rank and file of the army than in their captains and commanders; in those who did the work rather than in those who designed and planned it. Such horny-handed men obviously fascinated him for, whether at work or resting or eating their meals, he photographed them indefatigably. To some of his subjects, his camera was obviously a new and strange device, for they responded to Newton's request to pose self-consciously and with varying degrees of suspicion. Yet when we remember the necessity for a long exposure, it is a tribute to Newton that so many appear so natural and at ease. The photographer was obviously able to win their confidence. The majority gaze boldly at the camera, proud of their work, yet surprised that anyone should wish to record them.

We are apt to call all railway builders 'navvies' whereas the term properly applies only to the men who shifted 'muck' with pick and shovel, but, as Newton shows us, there were many men of diverse skills besides: bridge gangs, bricklayers, steel erectors and riveters, miners, blacksmiths and enginemen. Yet, as the following pictures reveal, there was still plenty for the famous British navvy to do. Despite the use of steam-powered machines, railway construction was still what a modern economist would call a labour-intensive undertaking. Steam power might gnaw its way through high ground with an ease and rapidity unknown in the old days, but an army of navvies had to follow in the wake of the steam exacavators in order to trim back the cutting slopes, a job which machines were still powerless to do. The job had to be done speedily, too, otherwise the gashes made by the machines, with their near vertical sides, might very soon fall in behind them. So, in this transitional phase of civil engineering construction, there was still plenty of work for the navvy even though it was no longer entirely dependent on his efforts. But after the Great Central had been completed no similar work of comparable magnitude was undertaken in Britain until the building of the motorways sixty years later; a few small extensions here and there, some 'cut-offs' built by great railways – most notably by the Great Western – which were anxious to shorten and improve their existing main line routes, but nothing of the magnitude of the London Extension of the Great Central. For this reason, the men depicted here represent the last generation of a mighty race whose Herculean achievements, written across the face of England in earthwork, masonry and iron, survive for us to marvel at. So we should be grateful to Newton for the fact that he was at such loving pains to record them for posterity. But for him we should not know what manner of men they were. It is a unique record; did the photographer or his subjects realize that their time was running out, that they were writing the final chapter?

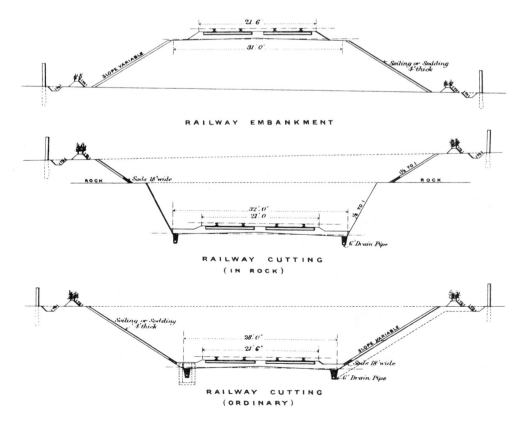

RAILWAY EMBANKMENT

RAILWAY CUTTING
(IN ROCK)

RAILWAY CUTTING
(ORDINARY)

ABOVE
The 'Paddy Mail' takes the men to their work
RIGHT
Foreman Marchment of Hillmorton and his wife
outside their hut at Woodford Camp
BELOW
Steel erectors near Wilford, Notts.

ABOVE
Rivetting gangs with a foreman standing left in the
left-hand picture
RIGHT & BELOW
Steel erectors at Leicester. A navvy Missioner is
standing under the crane jib at Braunstone Gate
bridge, Leicester in the picture below

A bridge construction gang near Blaby, Leics.

LEFT
Miners driving a heading near Saunderton on the joint line

BELOW LEFT
Blacksmiths in their shop at Mowmacre Hill depot, Leicester. From sharpening picks or shoeing horses to forging a new part for a machine, there was always plenty for them to do

ABOVE & BELOW
The pump attendant and the signalman

LEFT
A one-legged watchman near Staverton Road
ABOVE & BELOW
Horse-leaders and horse boys on the Wotton
Underwood to Haddenham section. Notice the
wooden sprags used to lock the wheels of the wagons

Temporary way men

94

LEFT
Laying piped drains beside the line near
Loughborough
BELOW
Trans-shipping ballast, Charwelton depot
BOTTOM LEFT & RIGHT
Laying rubble drains in the cutting sides

Cutting back or trimming cutting sides

ABOVE LEFT & RIGHT
Groups at Nottingham and Leicester
LEFT
On the boundary between the Northern and Southern Division, Rugby. The most southerly group working on Topham, Jones & Railton's contract
BELOW
At Wembley Park, the Metropolitan tower can be seen in the background

ABOVE LEFT & LEFT
Near Haddenham, Bucks.
ABOVE
At Wotton, Bucks.
BELOW
On the site of Marylebone

Navvies at rest. 'Grub up'. Lower picture shows an
old cellar at Nottingham adapted as a shelter.
Although he was now provided with living
accommodation, making shelters and huts had
become as instinctive to the navvy as nest-building to
a bird

ABOVE LEFT & RIGHT
Lunch break at Sulgrave and Brackley
RIGHT
Tea break at Albion Road, Kilburn
BELOW
Annie and navvies take a breather south of Rugby

ABOVE
Group outside their hut at Leicester
BELOW
A break for bread and cheese at Wilton Park,
Beaconsfield, on the joint line

8 *The Alternative Route*

Newton also covered with his camera the construction, undertaken in partnership with the Great Western, of the new line from Neasden to Grendon Underwood which gave the Great Central an alternative route into Marylebone independent of its earlier partner, the Metropolitan. He concentrated his attention mainly on the two sections of the new railway over the chalk of the Chilterns which necessitated the heaviest works. The first of these was that portion of the new line between Beaconsfield and High Wycombe which included Loudwater Tunnel and much heavy cutting and embanking. At High Wycombe this new line joined the existing Maidenhead–Aylesbury Branch of the Great Western Railway, and the second section on which Newton concentrated consisted of the doubling of this single line between High Wycombe and Princes Risborough. Here the widening of the Wycombe Viaduct and considerable re-alignment was required to bring the old route up to main line standards. The engineers decided to use the existing line between Saunderton and Princes Risborough, where it descends steeply from the chalk escarpment into the vale, for down trains and to construct the new 'up' line on an entirely different alignment involving a tunnel and heavy chalk cuttings so as to ease the grade for London-bound trains.

The existing stations at the Wycombes, Saunderton and Princes Risborough were completely reconstructed. As Newton's 'before and after' pictures of Princes Risborough show, the platforms were set back to allow two additional tracks to be laid in the centre for through traffic. The new stations on the section south of High Wycombe were built upon the same model.

RIGHT
Climbing the Chilterns: the new 'up' line formation
looking south from the top of the tunnel. The course
of the 'down' line can be seen on the right
BELOW
Tunnel on the new 'up' line alignment between
Princes Risborough and Saunderton

RIGHT
View of the works looking north from the top of
Loudwater Tunnel in the direction of High Wycombe
BELOW
The new Loudwater Tunnel, south end

109

LEFT & BELOW
Princes Risborough Station after and before. In the left-hand picture the new fast lines have not yet been laid
RIGHT
Widening works. Looking north towards Wycombe Viaduct

ABOVE
Widening works beginning at the north end of High Wycombe old station. Notice the distinctive GWR 'baulk road' – bridge rail on longditudinal sleepers – a survival from the great days of Brunel and his broad gauge

LEFT
The line as it was. Looking south towards High Wycombe
RIGHT
Widening the Wycombe Viaduct
BELOW
Widening works completed

9 *The Stations are Built*

At the time the London Extension was conceived, Alexander Ross, one time assistant engineer to Robert Stephenson, was Chief Engineer to the Manchester, Sheffield and Lincolnshire Railway. Although by the time work on the Extension began, Alexander Ross no longer occupied that post, all the stations on it were built to designs prepared by him. Together they present what is perhaps the most original and certainly the most characteristic feature of the new railway.

With the exceptions of the two-platform stations at Carrington and Arkwright Street, Nottingham, and the new London terminus at Marylebone, all stations, urban and rural alike, have island platforms between the 'up' and 'down' lines. In the case of Nottingham Victoria and Leicester Central Stations, these island platforms are of great length and breadth to allow for the provision of double terminal bays within them. All these island stations are situated either on embankments or in cuttings at points where a road bridge crosses under or over the railway. In the case of the former, access from the roadway to the platform is via an ascending arched subway which was incorporated in the bridge structure. Similarly, where there is an overbridge, a descending arched stairway was formed in its broad central pier, a porters' lamproom being situated in the space below the stairs. Usually an entrance hall was built on the bridge at road level, but at Brackley the Corporation (as it then was) objected to the use of their road bridge for this purpose so the entrance building was sited at the head of a special approach road. In other cases, local authorities were more amenable and some agreed to the diversion of existing public roads in order to bring them adjacent to the station sites. Apart from the three main city stations, Loughborough, Rugby, Woodford and Brackley, although of island design, were larger than the rest of the stations on the line which were all described as 'of the standard country type'.

Such was the optimism that the ambitious dream of Sir Edward Watkin engendered that Alexander Ross designed his stations with the eventual quadrupling of the new main line in mind. His idea was that the two additional fast lines could be laid one on either side of the station without interfering with their platforms or buildings in any way. For this reason the arches of the standard type of station bridge were designed to accommodate four tracks. Compared with the conventional design of railway station with its duplication of platforms and buildings, Ross's design was cheaper and easier to construct. As against this, however, it possessed the disadvantage that heavy luggage and passenger freight could not be readily conveyed to the platforms and to obviate this parcels lifts, hand operated at the smaller stations, had to be installed.

Of the main stations, Nottingham was built in a cutting between two tunnels whereas Leicester Central is situated entirely on viaduct. Nottingham station was to have been called 'Central' also, but its name was changed to 'Victoria' in deference to its joint owners, the Great Northern Railway. Such were the niceties of railway diplomacy. Nottingham station was opened without ceremony on 24 May 1900 – Queen Victoria's birthday an occasion which was commemorated by the striking of a suitable medallion. Curiously enough, apart from photographing this medallion, Newton does not appear to have taken many pictures of Nottingham Victoria station under construction although, as we have seen, he duly recorded other railway works in the area.

Although Newton photographed the building of Marylebone passenger terminus and hotel, he failed to record fully the other buildings in the area which included stables to accommodate 650 horses on three floors (an equine version of the modern multi-storey car park), an electric and hydraulic power station, a rail/canal trans-shipment shed beside the Regent's Canal, Goods Offices and, lastly, the large goods warehouse which attracted much comment among civil engineers. This was a steel-framed building with curtain walls of brick 390 ft long by 261 ft 6 in wide, its five storeys providing a total floor area of nearly eleven acres. On its roof were two cast-iron water tanks with a combined capacity of 22,500 gallons for use in the event of fire. It was centrally heated throughout and equipped with hydraulic cranes, hoists, capstans and traversers. The company's workshops, locomotive and carriage sheds for the London area were built at Neasden and were similarly ignored by Newton.

When the London and Birmingham Railway was built, the first trunk line to enter London in 1838, the terminal site chosen was to the north of the Euston Road, 1¾ miles from the heart of the metropolis, and each subsequent railway advancing on London from the north followed suit, accepting this and Marylebone Road as a boundary beyond which it was imprudent to advance. Consequently, by the time the late-coming Great Central arrived, the site chosen for their station, immediately to the west of Regent's Park, was the only practicable one left. Even so, owing to the nineteenth-century growth of London, it involved considerable demolition of property and diversion of streets, both expensive operations. Especially so since more land was acquired with an over-optimistic eye to future expansion than was actually needed.

That a large city station should have a single-span all-over roof, thus leaving the platforms clear of columns, had become an established Victorian convention which the last newcomer, the Midland Railway, had accepted in magnificent style at St Pancras. That the engineers of the Great Central chose a glazed pitched roof with spans of moderate size rising from steel columns mounted on the platforms therefore occasioned considerable controversy. They defended their design by saying that it achieved the desired end with much greater economy of means and that, on such wide platforms, the steel columns caused no inconvenience. Also that their terminal had been designed with expansion in mind, possessing a flexibility which a great all-over roof lacked.

As built, Marylebone was certainly small. It had two arrival platforms divided by a cab road and a single double-faced platform for departures served by five lines. But provision had been made for doubling the size of the station and these additional tracks and platforms are hopefully shown dotted on contemporary plans of the terminus. Alas, these were never needed. Born too late, Marylebone never grew up.

LEFT
Medal commemorating the opening of Nottingham Central Station (re-named Nottingham Victoria) in 1900
BELOW
Loughborough station at an early stage of construction

LEFT
Leicester Central: the station portico nearing
completion
BELOW
Leicester Central Station under construction
RIGHT
Leicester Central: entrance to a Roman pavement,
preserved *in situ*, beneath the south end of the station.
The pavement has recently been moved to Jewry Wall
Museum

RIGHT & BELOW
Goods station at Braunstone Gate, Leicester

RIGHT
Rugby station newly completed, 1899

ABOVE
Forming the island platform for Ashby Magna Station
LEFT & BELOW
Willoughby, an 'overhead' type of country station,
and its entrance, formed in the abutment of the
underbridge

FOLLOWING PAGES
On the summit of the line: Charwelton

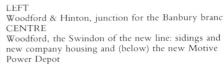

124

ABOVE
The drawback to Ross's island platform design is well illustrated in this picture of Calvert Station. The rather makeshift platform in the foreground was used for loading milk churns

LEFT
Building the station hotel at Marylebone. It was built
by a separate company, was renamed the Hotel Great
Central and is now the headquarters of the British
Railways Board
RIGHT
Marylebone Station buildings under construction

ABOVE
Site for Marylebone Station after clearance
LEFT
Floor columns, Marylebone goods station
FACING PAGE TOP LEFT
Erecting steelwork for Marylebone goods station
FACING PAGE TOP RIGHT
Putting roof trusses on to columns, Marylebone
passenger station
RIGHT & FOLLOWING PAGES
Marylebone passenger station nearing completion

10 The Permanent Way is Laid

As the works neared completion the wavering and roughly laid contractors' lines consisting of flat-bottomed rail spiked to old sleepers began gradually to disappear. First on one side and finally upon the other it gave place to the permanent way advancing on its properly ballasted formation.

On the natural formation a layer of hard, rough stone pitching was first laid, each stone being 9 in deep and laid on edge. On top of this came a layer of coarse gravel of the same hard stone broken sufficiently small to pass through a 2 in ring. The effect of this was to seal the interstices between the stone pitching and so prevent the top ballast from working through. The quantity of stone used in this way was 7,500 cu yd per mile of double line.

In clay districts this procedure was varied somewhat. In soft clay cuttings a two-inch 'blanket' of burnt clay, clinker ballast or coarse gravel was first laid to keep the formation dry and prevent the stone pitching from sinking into the clay. On the higher clay embankments from 12 to 15 in of burnt clay ballast was used in place of the stone pitching. For the top ballast, 2-in broken ironstone slag from the neighbourhood of Hunsbury Hill, Northamptonshire, was extensively used. This was either loaded into trucks at the ironworks by hand, using forks with prongs three-quarters of an inch apart, or it was passed through suitable revolving screens to rid it of all dust and small stuff.

On this foundation the creosoted sleepers measuring 9 ft by 10 in by 5 in were laid out and drilled to receive the 52 lb chairs which were each secured by two iron spikes and two trenails. Into these chairs the new steel rails, each 30 ft long and weighing 86 lb per yard were dropped, secured with oak keys and fishplated together. Finally, this new permanent way was aligned horizontally and vertically by slewing and by packing or 'tamping' ballast beneath the sleepers. The above figures apply to main running lines; on sidings 38 lb chairs and 75 lb rails were used.

On all major bridges and viaducts, old rails weighing about 65 lb per yard were laid on their sides and employed as guard rails. These were bolted to the projecting brackets of a special type of chair weighing 93 lb that had been designed for use in such locations.

At a time when the L&NWR had been using 60 ft rails on its main line for many years and most other companies were laying rails of 45 ft, it may well be asked why the engineers of the Great Central specified rails of so short a length for their new main line, thus 'spoiling the ship'. To this there is no satisfactory answer. When Francis Fox presented his Paper on the construction of the Southern Section of the line to the Institution of Civil Engineers, W.R. Galbraith asked this very question in the discussion that followed the reading. He received the unsatisfactory reply that 30 ft was the standard length used elsewhere on the Manchester, Sheffield and Lincolnshire system, a curious example of 'nothing like leather' mentality.

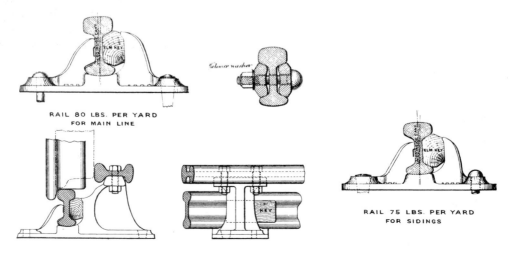

RAIL 80 LBS. PER YARD
FOR MAIN LINE

RAIL 75 LBS. PER YARD
FOR SIDINGS

LEFT & ABOVE
Laying the stone pitching
BELOW
Coarse gravel is laid over the stone pitching

ABOVE
Packing and levelling the new track
BELOW LEFT
Drilling sleepers for the chairs at Finmere
BELOW
Ready for the rails
RIGHT
Accompanying the permanent way men were the company's telegraph linesmen. This picture of one of their vans is Newton's only record of them

137

11 *The Line is Opened*

On 25 July 1898 coal trains began using the new railway. Such slow-moving and heavy traffic served to 'iron out' and consolidate the road. Eight months later, on 15 March 1899, the first express passenger train steamed out of Marylebone. It carried only four passengers, which is scarcely surprising in view of the fact that it left at 5.15 in the morning. For the 9.15 train fourteen passengers turned up and for the 1.15 p.m. the complement was thirty-four, while for the 5.15 p.m. express, which included a dining car, fifteen first-class seats were reserved. 'These results,' remarked *The Railway Magazine*, 'are regarded as eminently satisfactory.' It is not clear, however, whether the magazine was giving its own opinion or quoting some loyal company official determined to look on the bright side.

It is really no wonder that traffic was thin. In Victorian England fierce railway competition was accepted as one of the facts of life. It was argued that the public would benefit even if the shareholders suffered. But whereas in the past even the most militant companies had been content to fight on only one front at a time, on its new London Extension the Great Central had to battle for traffic against no less than three powerfully entrenched adversaries: the Midland, the Great Northern and the London and North Western. Moreover, the Great Central was initially handicapped by the fact that the embankments on its new line had to be given more time to consolidate before it could seriously join battle by introducing express train timings that were genuinely competitive.

Although the London Extension, as we can now see, was hopelessly over optimistic and bound to be a failure commercially, that the company so soon justified its grandiose new title and earned the public respect which enabled it to win a sizeable share of the traffic from such powerful rivals was due above all to one man – the General Manager Mr (later Sir) Sam Fay. Sam Fay had earlier won the admiration of the railway world by his management of the Midland South Western Junction Railway which had transformed that near-bankrupt concern into an efficient and modestly thriving minor railway. The Great Central directors could not have picked a better man. Fay was a great administrator and but for his energetic and aggressive management the London Extension might have proved a far more disastrous white elephant than in fact it was. Under Fay a service of fast, comfortable and punctual express trains was introduced which soon established the company's reputation with the public. He was also responsible for introducing an extensive network of through carriage services, working to their destination over other companies' lines. Backed up by an advertising campaign unusually vigorous for a railway company of the period, these services gave the public the impression that the Great Central system was far more extensive than it was in reality. You could travel by Great Central coaches to places as far apart as Torquay, Swansea, Aberystwyth, Llandudno, Blackpool, Halifax, Scarborough and Newcastle. It is also worth mentioning that overseas visitors wishing to pay homage to Shakespeare at Stratford-upon-Avon could then speedily travel thither by a through carriage from Marylebone which was handed over to the East and West Junction Railway (later the Stratford-upon-Avon and Midland Junction) at Woodford. It is now impossible to travel from London to Stratford by through carriage and only the most tenacious railway traveller would choose to make such a journey.

Sam Fay's policy of fast and punctual running would have been nullified had he not possessed the motive power to achieve it and here his tremendous drive was matched by the outstanding ability of his colleague, the Locomotive Superintendent, John G. Robinson. At the time the London Extension was opened, Harry Pollitt was Locomotive Superintendent. On the assumption that traffic on the new line would be light, Pollitt designed two express passenger locomotives for service on the London Extension, a single-wheeler and a 4–4–0. The former type was one of the last 'singles' to be designed for service on a British railway and, even granted the featherweight trains of the early days, it was somewhat optimistic. The new line might be eminently suitable for singles, but not so the steeply graded Metropolitan route over the Chilterns where, under a combination of adverse conditions, they could easily get into difficulties.

John G. Robinson was Swindon trained and, like Aspinall and Ivatt, he had cut his wisdom teeth in Ireland before he succeeded Pollitt at Gorton in 1900. He began modestly by producing a slightly enlarged version of the Pollitt 4–4–0, but he soon showed that he was an artist of locomotive design when, in 1903, the first of his famous outside-cylinder 'Atlantics' appeared. It is one of these engines that features on p. 000 of this section, caught by Newton's camera as it was passing over Charwelton troughs at speed. Such was their beauty that they were nick-named the 'Jersey Lilies'. Remaining in office until the Great Central lost its separate identity, the 'Atlantics' were the first of a long line of fast, powerful and surpassingly handsome locomotives with which Robinson endowed the railway.

By 1904 the new line had settled down and it was then that, with Sam Fay in command and Robinson supplying the motive power, the Great Central really began to show its competitors what it could do. Marylebone to Leicester was covered in 8 min less time than the Midland expresses operating over a route 6 miles shorter. The 4.30 p.m. express from Marylebone was scheduled to cover the 34 miles from Woodford to Leicester at an average of a mile a minute, start to stop. The 165 miles from Marylebone to Sheffield were covered non-stop in 177 min, an improvement of 6 min on the best Midland time. Later this express service stopped at Leicester and Nottingham with no reduction in the overall time.

Owing to speed restrictions on the Metropolitan Railway, 50 min had to be allowed for the 44½ miles between Marylebone and Quainton Road, a fact which makes such fast city to city times all the more meritorious. They entailed some extremely fast running over the new portion of the London Extension. For example, 'up' expresses were scheduled to cover the 58¾ miles from Leicester to Quainton Road at an average of 64 mph, start to pass. Such figures make it easy to understand the company's decision to build, in alliance with the Great Western, an alternative route which would by-pass the Metropolitan.

ABOVE
HRH the Duchess of Albany arriving at Charwelton
in May 1905
LEFT
Passenger Booking and Enquiry Office, 25 Gallowtree
Gate, Leicester

ABOVE & BELOW
4-4-0 locomotives designed by Harry Pollitt handled the express trains on the London Extension immediately after the opening in 1899. Here are two of them passing Brackley station and (below) nearing Leicester heading north
RIGHT
Charwelton water troughs

LEFT
Robinson 4–4–2 and 4–4–0 pick up water from Charwelton troughs
BELOW
Robinson 4–4–0 heads a northbound cross-country express, with GWR rolling stock at Leicester Central

RIGHT
The Woodford shedmaster and his staff pose proudly
with an immaculate Pollitt 4–4–0
BELOW
Inside the new loco shed at Woodford

12 *The Railway Men*

When the signals 'came off' for the first time on the new railway and the first trains came through, Newton's consuming interest in his fellow men again showed itself. Earlier, he had photographed the men who had built it; now he recorded the men responsible for running it. He was not so interested in the trains themselves as in those who kept their wheels turning and for this we should be grateful. For while the fascination of the steam locomotive attracted an enthusiastic army of photographers from its earliest days to its passing in the 1960s, few thought of recording the contemporary railway man for posterity and surely none with such affectionate thoroughness as did Newton.

In 1900, the smooth and efficient working of a great railway still called for the largest and most intricate organization that man had ever evolved. Sir Sam Fay's office at Marylebone (the headquarters of the company moved thither from Manchester in 1905) was the apex of a great pyramidal hierarchy held together by discipline and loyalty. The emphasis was on loyalty, on pride in the company and in the job, for where that quality is present discipline becomes self-discipline. From the General Manager's desk at Marylebone the invisible chains of command stretched away down the line, passing through his Superintendent of the Line to the signalmen in their lonely cabins high on the Northamptonshire wolds; to the locomotive men at Neasden and Woodford; to the stationmasters, guards and ticket examiners and so down to the humblest porter, wheel-tapper or permanent way ganger.

From Sir Sam Fay downwards, Newton photographed railwaymen of every rank and the pictures which follow represent about half the total. They reveal to us what manner of men they were. The stationmaster of Charwelton looks, in his smartness and pride, as though he were the master of some great London terminus instead of a remote rural station. Yet all of them, down to the humble wheel-tapper, seem to radiate the same enviable air of certitude and calm self-assurance, very proud and conscious of the fact that they were serving a great company. They do not look like miserable economic animals, ground down by their greedy capitalist exploiters and eager to rebel as some would have us believe. The London Extension had been built. The navvies passed on; to them it was just another job and they were not to know that it was one of the last. These were the men who moved in as the navvies moved out. Over the years to come it was they who made the railway justify its new title – Great Central.

LEFT
General Manager off duty: Sir Sam Fay in his garden
at Gerrards Cross
RIGHT
Mr Mosley, Superintendent of the Line
BELOW
Booking Office staff, Leicester Central

LEFT
Mr Kinch, parcels clerk, Leicester
BELOW
A Ticket Examiner sets the train indicator at Leicester

ABOVE
P.C. Milburn, Railway Police, Leicester
BELOW LEFT
A Passenger Guard

ABOVE
Mr Banyard, goods guard, at Leicester Horse Dock
BELOW CENTRE
The stationmaster, Charwelton
BELOW RIGHT
The carriage lampman

LEFT
Porters at Leicester
RIGHT
Woodford: (above) the station staff and (below) the
shedmaster and his staff

LEFT
The wheel-tapper
BELOW
The signalman, Calvert

RIGHT
Porter, Leicester, with portable water tank for
replenishing dining cars
BELOW
A permanent way gang near Chetwode, Bucks.

Railwaymen off duty: the stationmasters of Woodford
and (below) Charwelton with their families pose for
Newton outside their new company houses

154

GREAT CENTRAL
RAILWAY COMPANY.

Programme
of
Arrangements
for the
CEREMONY OF OPENING
THE
EXTENSION TO LONDON
RAILWAY
at
Marylebone Station.

March 9th   · 1899 ·